Herbie's Here to Stay

by
Carol Staines

Pinedale Press

By the Same Author:

Books
A Very Practical Guide to Interior Decorating
How to Make Money from Your Hobby
Profitable Hobbies & How to Market Them
Take Me Back to the Eighties (text only)
The Hopeless Cooks Cook Book
The Hopeless Cook Entertains

Booklets
Lost in the Wilderness
Nurturing Your Dream
Understanding Australian Country Culture
Walking into the Sunlight (Guidance for those suffering bereavement)
Walking into the Sunlight Daily Readings

Published by Pinedale Press
Text and illustrations
© 2011 Carol Staines
All rights reserved

National Library of Australia
Cataloguing-in-publication data
Staines Carol, 1945
National Library of Australia
card number and
ISBN 978-0-9593024-6-2

1st Edition July   2011

Holder of Copyright

Pinedale Press
2 Lethbridge Court
CALOUNDRA QLD 4551
AUSTRALIA

For Orders: please fax (07) 5491 9219

Acknowledgements

To Deanna Van Duyn for her computer skills in preparing this material.

To Yvonne Schuiling for the cover photograph of her dog Willma. The winning photo in the British BBC Photo Competition.

Cover and book design by Deanna Van Duyn and Allan Staines.

Stardust Fell that Night

My life has been transformed and in a single, blissful moment. A rags to riches story you might read about in any newspaper. 'No,' others would argue, 'you were in the right place at the right time, that's all.'

Really, it doesn't matter because right now, I'm living it up how you wouldn't believe. Last week, or was it in a previous life, my lot was a threadbare and, I might add, smelly piece of towelling for a bed; for sustenance, a scrap of pizza or something spat out by some inebriated bum or at the best, a discarded, half eaten sausage left on the barbecue in the local park. It had been that way for a long time which was all I can remember about myself.

Then, it happened; I was "discovered" and heaven came down.

It was raining and I'd crept into a shed because the door was open. Just the spot to recoup, so I tucked in under the bench almost out of sight having learned it pays to stay inconspicuous. It was cosy and I must have dozed off. That was until two glaring lights and an engine roar spelt danger.

I'd always dreaded being flattened by a car, imagined lying on the road, abandoned, frightened, hurting until dead. The lights closed in along with the engine. Then silence. Is that what being dead does to you? Hear nothing, feel nothing? Then the garage lights flashed on. There was nowhere to run. A car door opened, then an angel's voice: 'There's a darling dog-gy hiding behind the bench. Look, "T", it's frightened.'

Aha…my senses were alert to every nuance.

Not an "animal", not a "mongrel", but the caressing voice of an angel saying, "darling dog-gy."

So I did what a dog-gy is supposed to do: wagged my tail, gave a gentle bark and hoped for the best but ready to dash for the door if necessary. The angel came closer, she reached out a hand. I was cornered. In a moment of desperation and seeing no other way out, I licked it. Timidly at first. That could at least provide a bargaining chip if necessary.

'Little dog-gy, are you lost?' she said, now patting my head then coaxing me out. There was no choice but to yield. Creeping at first. Once out, the deep voiced one with the beard; she calls "T", didn't yell: *Get that mongrel out of here!* My usual experience, and his boot didn't sink into my ribs. Instead, the stardust fell— He disappeared then returned with a plate upon which sat a lump of juicy steak and that was only the beginning.

Now my fortunes have reversed and this dog-gy is ensconced in comfort, and I'm hoping, with my probation period about expired, a valued member of the family. But of course that will come with certain privileges but also responsibilities.

Blood and Bone Will Tell

Parents, without even trying, can influence your choice of career. You can end up doing something that doesn't appeal in the slightest. Your genes take charge and you got no choice in the matter.

Take my Pop. He's a vague shadow in my life. A come-and-go type of fellow with not much affection for we young'uns and leaving all our rearing up to Ma. But a top notch bodyguard, or so I was told. Strong hind legs, quick reflexes, good jaw, big teeth and a nose to die for. All the bitches ran after him if Ma is to be believed.

'He could run for miles, tracking, scenting and hunting. "You're just like him, Herbie,"Ma always said. Well, I didn't want to take after him. Didn't want to be a bodyguard, preferred a pampered indoors life. With five or six siblings, can't remember exactly, you didn't get much of the tender side of Ma's tum. One minute you'd settle in for a good suckle, the next you find yourself upside down on the ground. So after a time I ran away. No one was going to push *me* around anymore. I'm afraid that was my first mistake.

How many miserable years I padded the streets, I can't recall. It was a happy day when I met "L" and "T". I admit to taking a good look at "T" after the initial introduction as I'd been kicked a few times by those who wear boots and have hairy faces, but he looked tolerable. The next challenge was how to ingratiate myself into their good favour and more importantly, turn it into a permanent arrangement.

My good luck came outdoors when "L's"

hat blew off in the wind. My Pa's genes took charge. I scudded after it across the grass, around some bushes, down a track heading toward the pond. I'd nearly reached it when another puff lifted it higher and closer to the water's edge. I leaped into the air, grabbed it then raced back and stood alongside "L" trying not to puff, and eyeballed her. She took it from me. The look in her eye said it all, but "T" wasn't such a push over.

'Just the body-guard we need,' "L" told him but I closed in on him and pawed his foot then slumped at his feet and eyeballed him. When you want sympathy, always show the whites of your eyes, the more the better. He stood stoical for a tense moment then bent down, slapped my flank and declared, 'you'll do me, fella.'

Then together we walked on. I was in the family.

People

Humans, although acting superior, are fragile creatures but what else could one expect with only two legs and such tiny teeth. Unfairly, they often resort to equipment with motors to assert their supremacy. They're so limited when it comes to sniffing. They also have some peculiar habits; some of which "L" and "T" are trying to foist on to me.

There's one they call "bath" but to make it more palatable, they talk in some kind of gibberish. That's another human trait. "Now sweetie,"(huh, I am not a lolly), "it's bath-ey time. You'll love it."

Oh, yeah!

After a few times, you can get used to it, even

find it a tiny bit enjoyable but it doesn't pay to admit to this because they'll go overboard and expect you to submit every week. So it's best to be a little uncooperative. Yelp as if the water is too hot, or give a shiver as if a little cold. At this stage, I'll tolerate this stupidity every two weeks but who knows?

A Day in the Life of this Bodyguard

Observation is a crucial part of my life. Right now I'm on duty hunkered down on rough ground screened by scratchy bushes and tormented by ants and zinging mosquitoes. It's hard work but someone has to do it and *that* someone is me. This, I realised one day when sprawled on the lounge floor watching TV.

Rex, the four pawed German, master crime-solver had, with his human offsider, rounded up the baddies as they were about to steal secret documents. He'd taken the man's wife as hostage, a gun to her head. Rex intervened.

Could "L", my Angel, because of "T's" work as an agent for a bank corporation, be at risk even at our so-called safe house—the address of which will not pass my lips—The problem was, she forgets about being watchful—I don't.

It is that sixth sense that, logically, cannot be explained, which is so important. I'd found that out, having roughed it in my previous life with its filthy alley-ways, freezing nights, smelly rubbish bins and dubious characters who wouldn't think twice about throwing a kick in the ribs.

No, there's no fond memories of that period. Not like now; a comfy bed at night, regular meals and affection for all my hard work. Who would want more? And when you get it, life is pure pleasure. Even better when there's a few treats and some tolerance of my foibles, of which, we all have our share.

I am now bodyguard to Agent "L" and Agent "T" as I like to refer to them. So, if one had to tread a rough path to reach this present utopia, so be it, but not only duty but love makes me care for their welfare. I can sniff out trouble, read their minds and know how to deal with troublemakers. That, I could truthfully say, is where my expertise lies. My C.V. is a satisfying read:

*Running and tackling: *excellent.*

*Aural warning ability: *authoritative and threatening.*

All very intimidating when other skills in my arsenal are also employed;

*Ability to track and tail: *practiced.*

*Alertness: *when necessary.*

Let me explain at this point, I'm a softy at heart. Not looking for trouble, I prefer to let life roll but not when my beloveds need protection. Which is why I've spent the last hour crouched behind this bush, ready to go on the offensive.

"L" walked past me not an hour ago and in her caressing way remarked, 'Herbie, it's cool under the bushes, take it easy.' I'm tempted to snort but refrain.'You're not aware, there could be danger and I'm on duty.'

Maybe it's better she doesn't realise there's audio waves humming down the footpath that need investigating. A put-put kind of motor steered by a man who prefers footpaths instead of roads. That, in itself, calls for observation but she remained in blissful ignorance.

Then it dawned, having recalled a TV show "T" watches. All secret agents have a place where intelligence can be exchanged. It's a smart move for "T" to have one with a slot facing the street as if it was nothing in particular. A put-put man has called here before and put something into "T's" dead letter drop. I've had him under surveillance for quite a while but I've seen both "L" and "T" withdraw envelopes, stare intently at the message, sometimes smiling, other occasions, frowning. I've even seen "T" rip an envelope open then stomp off with black words issuing forth while he read it then roar off in the car. I keep well out of his way when he's like that.

This time it's a new courier. Is he legitimate? He stops his machine by the dead letter drop, glances around…reaches into a bag on the put-put, fiddles. My muscles tense, my brain unable to decipher the message then he withdraws something, reads it, puts it back then moves on down the street. Had there been a dereliction of duty on my part? That had to be pondered, then I recalled: He wears the same uniform as the other put-put man. On consideration, there was nothing that required an immediate response. It's a relief to move from this uncomfortable position. Yet, having been on guard on what could have been 'an incident' was fulfilling.

Tomorrow will be a full-on day as "L" will be

alone; her beloved, "T" has, in the call of duty, flown off somewhere north. I know; I was listening. Something about the office where he works in an important position where they depend on his expertise; where he's privy to secrets that involve large amounts of money and…pity, he moved away and I didn't catch what could have been the juicy part.

Could be top secret when you consider the location he's been assigned. Right now, I'll recruit my energy and see what eventuates. *Wonder what's for supper tonight?*

Critical Duties

Official bodyguard duties are complex requiring opposing skills to function successfully. It's like splitting your brain in two then deciding which half to use after considering the potential threat. In case you are sceptical, let me explain.

I am supposed to be alert at all times, that's an industry given, but at the same time, not to appear alert. Relaxed but also tense, ready to spring into action in a split second if required. To observe but not to be observed. To be a nothing yet to be a critical somebody. This is not easy. One either becomes spooked by shadows or the mind drifts when counter attack is necessary. Intuition without substance is vital but so is logic demanding evidence. A lot of our work depends on what our industry calls questionable or suspicious movements which may or may not occur. That variable means hours of mindless waiting around for which the few, but critical moments of action, must compensate for the boredom. It is time to bare my soul—

In spite of these contradictions I like my job, the adrenalin rush but mainly the love from "L" and "T". This has started me to reminisce. To recall the 'Energex' emergency. It was, if I modestly admit, a classic piece of body-guarding. I had been camped out on the verandah which is a good surveillance elevation from the road. "L" and "T" were still asleep having been out half the night. My preferred watch post would have been closer to them but they accuse me of snoring when off duty; not a believable statement but humans are apt to make such exaggeration. By the way, *they* also snore but this bodyguard doesn't have the heart to reveal classified inside information. Now that's another role of a bodyguard—no gossiping or selling inside stories to the media—My lips are sealed.

It wasn't a stand-out morning. Nor a particularly sunny one, or a bitter cold one, rowdy or deathly quiet. Nary a hint of trouble but isn't that how it works in this industry? Two boring hours of doing nothing in particular and hoping for a spot of bother to add a little zing to the day. Maybe God in the sky heard these thoughts and decided to oblige. The only amusement so far was watching the crows teasing me by drinking out of my water dish and daring each other to dash in, sip and take off.

At first I didn't notice the signs of answered prayer. Then instinct raised an alert. Just a tickling sensation that could easily be ignored by a novice. I glanced up just in time to catch a moving shadow at the end of the driveway; which is quite steep and a little forbidding. The recesses of my brain advised that shadows don't methodically and quickly move forward. A sniff and I knew it. Trouble had arrived.

I sized him up—infantry style boots, long khaki pants and shirt, hat and a weapon in his hand. Something quite futuristic my ancestors would have said. A small black box, nothing more to identify it. Did it hold paralysing rays? Could it be a communicating device? A surveillance camera? Definitely suspicious. Did "T" and "L" realize they were being tagged?

By this time, the suspect had reached the side of the house and was closing in. It was time for action, muscles quivering: but first I quickly briefed up on the correct textbook bodyguard response plan. One: *a gentle warning*…Two:

*wait…repeat the warning…*Three: *purposefully move forward…*Four: *confront*, then, if necessary, Five: *decisive action.*

Steps one to three brought no response so I raised the decibels. That was ignored. Time for step four and confront. Now, that takes courage. Believe me, your life could be snuffed out at this point by a black thing with a small snout and a lump of lead or a ray gun concealed in the black box. I kept an eye on the man's trigger finger. Still, duty is duty. Sometimes I have nightmares about situations like this and imagine the eulogy over my grave. "L" and "T", naturally, would be devastated. Other bodyguards would miss me. Well, I hope they would.

Then I flew for him covering the distance from my den to the bottom of the driveway in a flash and was almost at his feet when he reacted in the most unusual manner. So unlike anything experienced to date. He yelled a half foreign language. 'Energex! Energex! You idiot—Stop!'

I pulled up sharp, took a few steps back keeping my eyes on his and those fingers on that black secret weapon. 'Energex! Energex!' again. Those words held meaning. My mind now racing…friend or foe? Is he Agent "E" for Energex? Whose side was he on?

I gave another audible warning, a growl from the back of the throat. He stood still, smiled a little but with a speck of fear in his eyes. I stood my ground struggling to reach a decision. Then, lost data from deep recesses rushed forward: *'Electricity Inspector, Okay to Pass'*. All the same I kept him under surveillance as he continued to the side of the house, lifted a lid, waved his black box about, dropped the lid and sauntered down the drive. Obviously another dead drop but maybe one used for special communications. Must record that on my internal register under "E". No ill feelings I hope. No one is perfect all the time.

Let the Truth be Known

There's a slight stirring of discomfort in my heart at the moment. Something has to be resolved with Agents "T" and "L". To *my* mind it reflects on my duties as a bodyguard and that's intolerable. To establish the facts, one must also consider *their* perspectives and motives. Could it have been their intention to be caring? Well, if it was, it wasn't well expressed. "T" and "L" sat in the lounge sipping coffee after work. I welcomed them in the usual manner and received acknowledgement in the usual manner. Routine can be quite reassuring.

They then discussed several matters, some obviously unpleasant by the expression on "T's" face. I let that pass because this occurs with my humans and I suppose with others. Then it happened. They impinged upon my dignity. The conversation flowed like this—

'"T", dear, don't you think that Herbie's getting a tad overweight,' "L" said, spreading a piece of toast with a generous layer of butter and jam.

'Needs more exercise, if you ask me.' "T" replied. 'All that lying about doing nothing.'

Of all the cheek! I tolerate that bath-ey thing and the balanced diet nonsense forced on me but references to my physical appearance is personal territory and not up for discussion. To communicate my displeasure, I gave a *hurrump* from the back of the throat—It had taken a lot of practice to perfect it—"T" looked up from the Bike magazine he was reading.

'What can we do about it,' "L" asked him.

'One meal a day, ' "T" replied as if it was of no consequence.

It mightn't be to him with his three meals a day plus in-betweens but it was to me.

But there followed more unsettling talk. 'Might help to put him on a diet and an exercise routine.'

'You're right,' "L" replied.

You're dead wrong, I thought adding another *hurrump* then foolishly thinking they might become busy and forget all this nonsense. But there's something about humans. They don't forget even when there's a time lapse in which you think something more important will distract them.

I spent a few hours brooding over their assessment of my shape and appetite. How would they feel if they were tied to all this surveillance and inactivity, then be expected to retrain and starve. Would they stay fit? Wouldn't they carry a bit of flab? Agent "T" has acquired a mid torso bulge so why pick on me?

I thought the matter was forgotten when "L" was knocked off her bike and hurt her ankle. It diverted *my* mind but it wasn't so with them. So it was with some surprise that next morning there was no breakfast left out for me. But to make sure it hadn't been misplaced, I padded out to the kitchen where there were two bowls and plates sitting on the bench; used ones. Number three bowl was missing. I checked the bedroom…empty, bed unmade. Nudged open the bathroom door, towel on the floor. Knew what those signs indicated.

An hour later nothing had changed. Two hours later, same situation. Then it struck. They'd not forgotten. It was deliberate. De-lib-er-ate—a diet conspiracy. Starvation until they came home from work. Did "T" miss out on his lunch? Didn't "L" take her usual salad roll and apple? Why pick on me? Then, out of nowhere, my previous life flashed back.

Breakfast in those days was a luxury. Was I becoming soft?

A few days later the rest of the conspiracy was put into effect—I was bundled off to Exercise School. Like being in the Army…*Halt! Turn! Sit! Stay! Run!* Fagged me out but I wouldn't admit it. Two more months of this treatment and I'll be a shadow. That night, collapsed in a comfy bed following a generous evening meal but without the trimmings; to which I am accustomed, and certainly no afters, the truth had to be confronted but not publicly admitted. They were probably right—Herbie was out of shape, just slightly of course—Besides, there's some cute wanna-be bodyguards on the course that need checking out. Might be worth pretending to enjoy Exercise School.

The C Word

There's been an elevation in my status and it's most gratifying. It did take a bit of masterminding but cunning and perseverance are my strong points. I was fed up with being ejected outdoors at night. Perhaps that's a little harsh, because it only occurred when I refused to budge and "T" took to using muscle. That's what gave me the idea—Make it preferable for them to leave me inside.

Firstly this involved a protest. A sort of "make your grievances heard", loud and clear, like long, drawn out whines for an hour after being ejected. It didn't work, even after a week of it and I was at wit's end with a sore throat before my lucky break came. "T" caught the flu and being confined in bed, miserable, lonely and receptive to gentle persuasion.

"L", running late for work, left the sliding door open, so naturally, I took advantage and quietly padded down the passage toward the invalid, half expecting to be bawled out, but he was snoring so I crept onto the mat beside the bed, then dozed. After a while I discovered a dangling hand stroking my head.

'Good boy, Herbie, come to keep me company have you?' I thumped a tail and made a moochy sound. From that point on, to my surprise, I found the sliding door ajar. By the time "T" had reached the television-lounge-chair-stage of recuperation, I was no longer just a backyard bodyguard but also a Companion.

With this elevation to additional intimacy with "L" and "T", night time surveillance is no longer restricted to the lonely outdoors but now includes creature comforts, TV viewing and additional nibbles. Getting to know them on this new level was my chance to sneak into their hearts and consolidate my new status but promotion has not gone to my head in so far as to neglect basic duties. Should they be threatened in any way, man-made or from the unpredictable elements of nature, you can count on me.

But there is a downside to this promotion. It has demanded an adjustment in attitude. In particular, the bath-ey one on which they are so determined. I now must surrender my grudge—human's sense of smell is so undeveloped. Possibly, in time, maybe in the hereafter, I'll enjoy the so called, fragrant wash from top to tail as the old saying goes. That is, as long as it doesn't happen too often or get out of hand to include extras. "L" is like that, she's into this beauty trap.

There is another slight downside to the companion role: "L" and "T" are not always in total agreement. It is not my place to take sides. Never fall for that trick if you consider yourself a good bodyguard/companion. Always stay impartial, giving loyalty or a cold shoulder to both parties. It has been known for married agents to fight over the affection of a bodyguard/companion and I don't intend that to happen.

It's important to train those to whom you have been assigned; not always an easy task. One that has to be done with a degree of cunning, and may I suggest, a little flair. To put them on a halter is not always quickly achieved but necessary. Sometimes they just take me too far, ignore me, blame me for stuff.

In this case, the disappearing act is the best solution. Preferably where they can't find you. Ignore any calls to 'heel', as they so rudely command; as if I was a common "dog". Play dead for as long as possible. It always works. When they discover how much they miss you, they'll panic—Ideal. Play dead a little longer until they become frantic. Give them time to repent, so they don't forget—Bodyguards don't come cheap.

Your next move must be well planned during the hours you have played dead. If possible, loop outside the property, limp back in with a hang-dog look and collapse at their feet. It's pure magic. They'll fuss over you and forget their previous disagreement with each other. Just one word of caution, don't recover too soon or there is a possibility they'll relapse into bad behaviour. Gradually open your eyes, whimper, stretch a little and lie very still. You may even earn a treat for this subterfuge. Certainly new respect. Just another warning. Don't try it too often; they might wake up.

Holidays

We're off, at last! I'm not complaining about waiting two hours for "T" to pack the luggage and for "L" to gather personal items, including tidbits for me (I hope). Nor am I complaining about being squeezed into the back seat with a large watermelon, a pile of ladies shoes (an aberration of "Ls") "T's" briefcase, board games, and a pile of books. What is more important is to somehow manage a snooze as bodyguard duties will be increased in a new environment. It could prove, for me, no holiday at all.

We're headed to some place called Lighthouse Point. To the camping ground to be more precise. A relaxing time for them but for me, fraught with challenges. "L" doesn't take

well to nature especially the creepy crawlies…
Then there are the bigger challenges: snakes,
dingoes, oversized bugs and lizards. A memory
from the last Frilly Lizard encounter, ghosts
through my mind. A reminder of what could
repeat on this holiday. I had expected to be
called a hero for my actions over that incident,
as any accomplished bodyguard would
agree but "T" was not of the same opinion.
"Disgraceful, cruel, irresponsible," were some
of his accusations. It hurt my dignity.

Oops, the car has suddenly swerved rolling
the watermelon into my ribs and sliding the
briefcase to the floor. What's in it? Why is
it coming with us? Is Agent "T" on another
special assignment? Are we meeting the
contacts out to sea on the dot of midnight? Are
they coming by plane then parachuting in?
Are they secret files, Russians or Money men.
But that's digressing. Frillies are quite arrogant

creatures, puffing out their ruff at the slightest provocation. As if that would frighten me although it might work with the timid. They scarper about the place as if it were their right. It was time to impose my authority, which is what happened but of course following standard bodyguard procedure…Stand your ground… warn (gently)…repeat (authoritatively)…take action (forcefully).

Frilly responded, maybe according to *his* standard procedure…stand your ground (puff up)…warn (hiss)…warn again (longer hiss)… take action (bite the offender).

So it became a battle of the wills. A gory business it ended up, but that wasn't my fault. The necessity of severing part of its tail was a goodly reminder not to mess with me. That's standard practice in the Godfather movies "T" likes to watch although those villains prefer a sliver of ear or a finger joint as the reminder.

There was certainly no need to bawl me out over a mere section of lizard tail. It was when "T" saw the body and a drop of blood, well, maybe a fair bit of blood, he really cut up. That, definitely, was not my fault. That lizard chose to bleed to death. He could have sued for peace terms but, no, the pesky fellow elected to fight on. Lighthouse Point is full of trees and probably full of frillies and that means full of confrontations and that means repercussions for me.

"T" swerves to miss a large pothole in what is supposed to be a road but more like a bush track to nowhere, like a scene from that movie 'At the Mercy of the Wilderness'. Not my preferred territory and the melon is about to roll on top of me yet again. This is too much... so is the thought of the creepy crawlies.

This bodyguard might have to go on strike, play dead or run away and have a holiday elsewhere and leave "L" and "T" to their fates. I'll stay within sight of their camp for any pickings. A few hours before they leave, I'll limp back into camp and plop down exhausted. That way there will be no repercussions and hopefully some tasty morsels as a welcome-home gesture.

Workers Rights

There are times when the glamour of my chosen occupation loses its gloss. Like being detailed for surveillance on a stormy night. Or after a hard working day, you run into a Miss Barbie poodle prancing down the street and she sneers at your supposedly scruffy appearance. Or when the weight of responsibility resting on my shoulders becomes oppressive. This time it was none of these, just sheer boredom.

Before you shake a finger of condemnation, this is a common malaise that, if you were honest, you'd admit to having experienced at some time. Didn't you also turn to the T.V. for solace?

With no one at home the house was deathly

quiet and with an absence of any sign of suspicious possibility to distract and the sun not yet reached a quarter of its path across the sky I picked up the remote and crunched it on. Hey, presto, action and noise, a bang, shoot-'em-up movie so I settled in, sprawled on the sofa. After the hero rode into the sunset and with no alternative relief from boredom, I continued to watch, even though it was some discussion panel about Workers' Rights. Eight hour shifts, tea breaks, work place health and safety, discrimination issues and how to take a stand against any infringement. It had me riveted. It was high time to examine my own employment status.

Under normal circumstances, it would not have crossed my mind to commit such sacrilege but lately there have been a few run-ins with "L" & "T.

For a start, "L" openly stated, at the same

time pulling a look of disgust, "Herbie, your breath is fetid, please stop yawning." Is that bullying? Lately they are out all hours in the car leaving me behind and forgotten. Neither have they discussed where they've been.

After that, I got into trouble for helping myself to the chicken pie left on the bench. How was I to know they were expecting visitors?

Some discussion about infringements of Worker's Rights was necessary. Calm, like, no biting on my part or retaliation from either side. Mid morning Saturday when they'd finally hauled themselves out of bed, read the newspaper and eaten breakfast, it would take place. There was the incident that, according to the specialist on TV, ought to become a written report and handed over but I won't go that far. The incident occurred at 5.30a.m. Saturday, 12th May and all in the line of duty.

I was dashing from one end of the property to the other to warn off an intruder. A sly cat who was trying to avoid me.

It took me closer to the edge of the house than normal. Being so focused on the task, I slammed into the edge of the casement window *they'd* carelessly left open. It gashed my leg, (liability on behalf of property owner), for which compensation is due.

Two hours at the medical clinic and six stitches later, we came home. "T" complained over the mere $200 he had to cough up. That was an insult. I know his useless motor bike in the garage cost $500 to repair when he hit a pothole and took to the air, so why go on about the accident *they* caused. Just like the TV programme said, unsafe work environments should not be tolerated.

The injury hurt so much I moaned in my sleep. It kept them awake, "L" complained, blaming me for the accident *they* caused. So they shoved me into the back room with no consideration for my injured state. It was definitely my responsibility to act on my Worker's Rights.

Of course it will have to wait till this leg heals. And really, I'd like more time to enjoy the radio they bought to keep me company and not to forget, "T" has promised to take me for a swim in the ocean. And "L" is still bringing me treats.

Maybe decisions on workers' rights will require further contemplation. Some things shouldn't be rushed.

Temptation

Agents "L" and "T" are up to something. "T" is getting the barbecue ready and "L" is in the kitchen pulling things out of the fridge. There's a plate of steak now sitting on the bench. S-t-e-a-k, tender pink and juicy and somehow I'm edging closer but then sternly remind myself of my duty. *Yes, but your duty doesn't include dead animals*, some wheedling voice in my head tempts. It's hard to resist that tantalising smell but somehow I manage it. "L" then walks out of the kitchen and down the passage. Then the devil voice in my head gets louder and my nose twitches.

Smells delicious, doesn't it? Dead animals need removal. That's your duty…Maybe they'll be pleased with you for taking care of that blood and fat? Maybe that's why it's sitting on the bench?'

I begin to salivate, noticing how close "L" has left it to the edge of the bench my muscles stiffen, there's a sudden urge to leap forward and remove the thing. It's my duty. I try to leave the scene but my feet are lead weights. Somehow I make it to the doorway but it's a struggle. I'm split in two.

It's hours since breakfast. Body-guarding is hard work and I deserve a treat. *They won't miss just one little steak,* the Devil voice hints. *Only this once…worry about the consequences later.*

Suddenly I'm hungry, my stomach growls and primeval instinct takes over but then an angel in my head starts on me, *That's stealing, Your sins will find you out.*

Just grab it and run, the devil urges. *It won't be missed.*

You're on trust, the other voice prodded, *a bodyguard…What you sow you reap. One little lie adds to another until it becomes a weight.*

Without realising it, I've inched back past the refrigerator and closer to the bench. Then I feel a presence enter the room. Is it the angel or the devil? It takes willpower to turn around, I'm a bit shocked even maybe disappointed to find "L" has come back to the kitchen. I try to look nonchalant and wander outside as if nothing had happened. Yet something did happen. I beat the Devil but it was a close call.

Bang...Bang

The sticky air makes me itchy and cranky. In another hour the sun will slink over the hill and peace will reign.

I had just slid into a beatific dream with coloured stars in the sky, kids laughing and running around when there was a horrific bang followed by another and another. I knew it. When all is well, danger stalks...Terrorists, anarchists, a bomb attack.

Where are "T" and "L"? Have they been caught unawares? Didn't they know of this? How come? They're the agents fighting crime? I'm just their bodyguard.

I skid into their room, panting and to be honest, shaking but that's only because I'd been asleep. Now I'm waking up, fast. It's time to sound an audible warning as required in the bodyguard handbook. Then another. They don't seem concerned so I run up to them and sound a further alert.

"T" responds at last. 'Herbie don't worry... it's nothing; just fire crackers.'

Crackers? Is that Agent Code? Well, it's not funny.

'Calm down, Herbie, you'll be O.K. Always fun to finish off the fete with fire crackers.'

Fun! Is that your idea of a good time. Bang, light screaming through the sky..bang..bang.

My legs are wobbly, my breath is coming in gasps and there's only one thing to do...Run! It won't do for all of us to be killed. Someone has to be a witness.

An adrenaline spike is giving wings to my legs. The back fence is no longer an impediment. I'm over it before I realise it's there. Run! Run! The brain chants, down the hill, plunging through the bush beside the creek driven on by more bangs. One whistles over my head, lands just ahead of me and explodes. Deafening, fuzzes my brain. I hit the dirt, shivering and yowling, can't help it. Incendiary colours lighten the sky.

If "L" and "T" don't know what is trouble, this bodyguard does. The war has started. I dig a hole with all my might and drop into it. It's the only shelter around and my best chance of survival, curled up but alert. Then fatalism takes over. If it's my time, there's nothing can be done about it. *Dear God, do you care for bodyguards?* I'm used to danger, but this is Armageddon. The rockets keep coming but I'm past caring. No use running. Just hope it's not a painful death.

I must have drifted off just waiting for the end. How come the sun is now up? Where am

I? I stand and stretch trying to get bearings. It takes a while but finally it dawns. I'm lost. Lost, lonely, and hungry. I hang around all day hoping to be rescued. Hope is fading. I've lost my home. Survive the bombing only to die alone. A tear forms in my eye and my throat of its own accord makes a whimper.

The sun is now well overhead as I lie and wait. Then I hear a sound, faint at first but growing louder. I lie low in case it's the enemy. Then again…'Heerrbee'. It's a woman's voice. Do they have front-line women soldiers now? Are they trigger happy? Playing dead is my only hope of survival. It comes closer 'Heerrbee'. My angel! My heart beats faster. Something surges within me and my body regains its strength, so, with a croaky voice, respond according to the text book: in the affirmative.

"L" and "T" gently lift me out of what could

have been my grave and onto the back seat of the car. I'm going back home…to heaven.

Parties

Not another invitation! I listen as "L" reads it with pleasure.

'Oh good,' she says, 'it's being held at the park at 2 p.m. Saturday.'

It's *not* good, I think. This party business I mean. Not good for me, her bodyguard, who is also an invited guest. I don't want to go.

Last time was enough. It's not the venue, nor the food but the guests. Well, some of them. I just have to think about that lot and it hardens my resolve never to go to one ever again. How could I forget the A.G.I. creature that came to the last one. Turned his nose up and down at everything. And I mean ev-ery-thing. A prima-donna beagle; nothing worse if you ask me. Sausages are cooking on the barbie so off he trots to suss it out. Then the ground had to be vacuumed by his super sniffer. After that he's checking out the lady's perfume then the men's, although, for some reason, it's called after-shave. Even had the cheek to sniff my tail. That was too much. I hedged up close to him to inspect the tag around his neck. A.G.I in large letters and underneath Authorised Government Inspector. I know that sort. We commonly refer to them as 'Sniffer Snouts' or 'Nosy Parkers' depending on how annoying they've been. 'This one,' the guests chatter, 'works at the Airport.' As if that was a status symbol. What does he do for all his airs and graces? Does he actually fly off to Europe or America on important business? Of course not. He just sniffs the luggage and *should* he, by chance, with that fine nose of his, find contraband, what happens? He gets a tasty reward and a pat on the head. Get's 'em all the time. Suppose he thinks he'll get 'em here. How about being a bodyguard for a change and doing something really important? Forget those childish treats and just do your duty.

"L" was enjoying herself talking to everyone while I followed her at a discreet distance. No threats here. Boring, more like it. Yak, yak, yak…eat, eat…drink, drink. After an hour I'd had enough and wandered to the sidelines trying to meet a nice chic or someone of my ilk but no such luck. Of course there was opportunity if one was inclined to mingle with the bikie type, of which there were a few. You know, the ones built like a tank, covered in jowl fur, and neck chains for jewellery. Wanna-be toughies. Greet you with a coarse growl; no refinement whatsoever. Nope, not for me. Nor do they have refined names like mine but coarse ones like 'Harlem', 'Cedric', even 'Butch'. Ever heard of such a crude name for one of my race?

As for other females in their club with their snooty, mincing ways, it staggers belief. No point hanging around them so I moseyed off back to "L" to give a gentle hint about leaving. The sooner the better.

'So this is *your* bodyguard,' a women sitting next to her blabbed and eyed me as if I were a street urchin. Not only lacking manners but definitely a Dill Brain.

'This is mine,' she said pointing to Poodle Face sitting demurely at her feet, nose in the air and totally useless. I sat down, put on a bored expression and gave a big yawn. 'Oooh,' what's your bodyguard been eating?' Dill Brain asked taking a pace backward. "L", smart agent that she is, took the hint and with a sweet smile replied, 'Garlic'. Together we walked off. And now she wants to go to another party!

Motor Bikes

Vrroom…Vrroom…"T" and I are watching the Dakar Rally on TV. I'm sprawled out on the floor because "T" has taken up all the couch. Doesn't that send a message about equality? But I'm not complaining because I wouldn't miss watching all that action for an..y..thing. Well, just about. It's exciting facing danger without raising a sweat. The close-ups of the driver's faces screwed up with tension makes me imagine we're a team. The two of us behind the wheel, dirt flying, wind in the face. Of course we'll beat the obstacles to the excitement of the onlookers.

The commentator is getting worked up, raised his voice and his words have speeded up as the bikes climb then tumble over the dunes. It's hot dusty work and along with him, "T" and "L" start panting as if we're truly competing in the race. "T" cools his thirst with a long swig of something. Nothing for me I notice. Is that equality? After all, we *are* a team.

Oops..there's been an accident before our very eyes. The wheels of the bike spin out of control and toss the driver off the machine. He hits the dust, rolls, rolls again, lays still for a moment. Is he dead? No, he rises, dusts himself down and mounts that cruel machine again. What happens next? We don't know. The programme has ended.

"T" emerges from the comfort of the couch and I trot after him into the garage. In the corner is one of his favoured toys. A sleek black and chrome machine with two special racing tyres and one long seat to take two people. Of course we're going for a ride. A kind of gentle pretrial for the Dakar. My muscles tremble in anticipation but there's only one bike helmet so who gets it? I stare at it wistfully. It is ignored while he fiddles with something. I add a whimper to ensure he gets the message that there's two of us. He keeps on fiddling with something on the handlebars. In the name of teamship one should offer mateship even if I'm just a bodyguard so I paw one of the tyres as though testing it.

'Herbie, don't do that.'

Well, I'm not listening either, so continue to add another mite of teamship.

'Herbie, that's the end! Get out and stay out.'

What a way to talk to me. As if I were a dog! Such behaviour is not to be tolerated. Should that bike be allowed to come between our relationship? Should I let it? It's my duty to do something about it.

Then, the last moment he's forgotten

something, keys probably and walks back into the house. This time I didn't follow but decided to assess that sleek machine; that hindrance to our relationship. My dreams have been shattered. No *vrroom vrroom* for me, only him. When I accidently brush against the wheel, I noticed that little pipe protruding near the tyre rim. A word from the world of espionage flicked through my brain. Action must be taken. Sabotage would make him realise the equality of our relationship must be respected. It has to be done. I chew on the little pipe until there's a *sssss* deflating sound then exit through the back door and collapse under a tree as if asleep.

"T" returns and yells something nasty which I pretend not to hear. He slams back into the house.

Next, the television is flicked on which means he's sprawled on the couch. It is my duty to creep into the house and normalise our relationship then flop on the floor beside him.

The Devil's Fault

Cockroaches have been the bane of my life as long as I can remember. If they're not getting me into trouble they are stealing food out of my bowl. I know there's very little left to steal after I'm finished, no matter, it's *my* bowl and no other critter is going to go near it.

Today I'm in the doghouse. Shunned by "T" and "L" which is not pleasant. Instead of basking in home comforts with them in the lounge there's just this miserable silence. Not even the radio for company. To think it wasn't even my fault. I lay all the blame at the feet of a pesky roach. Is that how the Devil plans it? Tantalises you and before you know it, you've gone along with him enjoying yourself with no thought of the consequences. Like ending up in the doghouse.

I would call myself a responsible bodyguard but does the Devil respect that distinction? Last Tuesday when "T" and "L" were out shopping, they allowed me to hang out on the verandah, my normal pad. They did, however, forget to shut the glass door to the lounge. That was the first mistake but it wasn't mine but does the Devil care about such fine points? So I squeezed into the lounge room and being responsible, chose not to use the comfy couch but lay on the floor which is cooler in this hot weather.

I'd just closed my eyes to have a snooze and was entering into that hazy no-man's land between sleep and wakefulness when there came a tickling sensation on my nose. Absently, I scratched to remove it. Instead it ran up the bridge of my nose, across one eyebrow, onto my head then back down my cheek into my jowls. I was up in a flash shaking my head until the tormentor dropped off. The meanest looking cockroach that would dare to come into this house. Before my very eyes it raced across the floor. I skidded after it but then it decided, at the prompting of the Devil most likely, to zip across the coffee table. I took a swipe at it as it rounded "L's" prize vase. It tilted sidewards, spilt the flowers and water then crashed onto the floor in pieces.

The cockroach then shot under a pile of "T's" top secret documents. That meant I had to paw through them to find him. Not a tidy operation especially in such trying circumstances.

By now you'd thought the troublemaker should have been ready to surrender or stop, gasping for breath but you'd be wrong. He was being urged on just to torment me. To be outwitted by that greasy midget was not on.

It then raced down the hallway and I was hot on the trail as it scooted up the wall. I swiped at it with a a sticky paw, but missed. Then it zipped down the passage and into "T's" study. I hesitated—that was forbidden territory but did the Devil worry about that? In went the greasy midget so I followed.

Now "T" may be very clever, but sometimes he's forgetful. It's all those decisions he has to make that tires his brain. So what did the greasy midget do? Crawled up the side of a coffee mug. Midget had almost reached the lip when I took affirmative action. How was I to know it was full of cold coffee? Or that it would pour across those papers and run onto the carpet. By now the greasy midget was firmly under my paw—dead. I was certain "T" and "L" would be most gratified and a special reward would be in the offing. Not on your sweet life.

Instead, now I'm being abused. No thank-you for getting rid of vermin which, I might add, "L" loathes. What did she say to me? "Herbie, look at this mess. Go to the doghouse 'til I tell you to come out." This ingratitude will be noted. They'll be sorry.

Lifestyle Balance

Everyone must have a break from the rat race and that includes bodyguards. That's *lifestyle balance* according to the TV experts. Work it into your every day commitments if you want to stay healthy. They do like using sophisticated words and complicated terminology. Why can't they be normal and say "work sometimes and play sometimes." Who would want to do anything else? For me, it's going outdoors communing with nature, sleeping under the stars, going for a run and swimming. Digging also releases pent up emotions.

Being a bodyguard is a walk-over or sit-over, the ill informed might deride. How far from the truth. When duty calls, yet again, and you're growing anxious but cannot leave your post to restore balance, act, but within the constrictions of your situation.

Last week everything became too much. "L" and "T" were away all day and most nights coming and going. The phone rang incessantly, someone came up the driveway, got out of the car, went to the door, knocked, slid something under it and took off in a hurry. In itself, suspicious. I had to paw it out and sniff for odors. It proved harmless although not pleasant, then somehow I replaced the slippery piece of paper. That alone, was fifteen tensious minutes with thoughts of arsonists, bombers, even kidnappers so popular these days. Does that also include bodyguard-nappers? You know what they do with them? Drug them and put them in the fighting ring. Then they bet on who's going to be the winner and have the cheek to call these dog fights!

I'd just settled down to restore my equilibrium when a possum landed on the roof, scampered along the verandah post then slipped and, with a bang, struck the sliding door. I was up there in a flash. Picked up the unconscious menace and hauled it to the edge of the garden and was about to wake it up, gently of course when glaring headlights interrupted the process. "T" and "L" were arriving home well after the midnight hour again. "L" was driving and obviously in a huff because "T" smelt of something like hops and they were having a tiff. Couldn't figure who was winning so decided to steer clear after making sure they were safe and sound, if not happy.

I woke up early next morning feeling ragged then realized my work/lifestyle balance must be out of kilter. Not being able to leave the premises was no excuse. The next best thing was to select a spot within the confines of the property and try to re-balance as advised by the expert. Gardening, now that would fix the fidgets so I began to dig a hole. In my agitation, I hadn't noticed those green things "L" called herbs. The activity lifted my spirits so I decided on another spot, a pretty one, by the petunias. Maybe it's that back-to-nature in all of us that comes to the fore and soothes the soul. Or is it the sense of accomplishment with dirt flying everywhere? The experts say it's the adrenaline rush from exercise that releases the endorphins. I dug a few more holes just enjoying myself and after that, lay down in the shade for a snooze. The expert was certainly right.

'Heerrbee! What's this!' "T", who had just arrived home, demanded in an angry tone. 'You've ruined "L's" herbs and petunias. Wait till she gets home and see's the damage. You're a vandal. Go to the Doghouse.'

He must have had a bad day at work. It happens to agents with their heavy work load and dangerous situations. One has to make allowances, so uttering not a word, I crept to the dog house to keep watch as it is conveniently sited outside and level with the kitchen sliding doors. Then I was alarmed to see him stomp inside the house, throw his briefcase on the floor (a bad sign) and take a bottle of beer from the fridge. Immediately following "L" arrived. What happened next I can't repeat and I didn't stick around to find out. It might upset my lifestyle balance.

Is it a Free Country?

I am being programmed, like it's a communist state. Re-educated they call it in Russia when you are deemed uncooperative and sent to a Gulag out the back of Siberia. You either freeze to death, are worked to death or re-educated to death.

It's more subtle in this country and more dastardly but now I have been awakened to the conspiracy, action is called for. It came to my attention of how it is propagated when I was sprawled out on the carpet watching television. "T" and "L" were similarly situated but due to their so called, superior status, on padded lounge chairs with feet up on the coffee table—Out of bounds for the likes of someone of supposed lowly status such as me. Humans are so unrealistic when it comes to evaluating priorities. You'd think dangerous guard dog duties would attract *all* the after hours perks.

They were goggle eyed before the box, silent, just sipping tea and eating a tasty biscuit. Well, I think it must have been, because they didn't offer me one. I saw two men who were locked up inside that box looking at us and acting normal. There was also a lot of other stuff; even cars although how they shrink to fit inside is a mystery. That's when it came to me that humans have magical powers.

The reprogramming of Herbie started in a refined manner, far removed from the blunt tactics employed in the blizzards of Siberia.

"T" came home a few nights ago carrying a book. He often does, but not a book like this one. How I discovered its insidious nature was the cover which enticed me to paw it open. The photos inside were shocking. A man bellowing out, I presume, commands like the Gestapo. *'Sit! Heel! Stop! Move!* I was paralysed with fear and could not help but paw further. *No sitting on chairs*, it stated, with a picture of a comfy arm chair and a black cross over it. *Eat before your dog. Be master*, it said. A clear case of "Me" first. The whole conspiracy to demote a poor dumb creature and lord it over him.

That book must be destroyed at any cost. It is my duty. I will not flinch. I will run away rather than become a pawn in a Communist conspiracy. Well, I will after dinner tonight because beef stew is on the menu followed by a spot of television and just as long as it's not dark and cold. Then a far superior idea wafted through my brain that will avoid such drastic measures: Fight back. Remove that evil book; it would be child's play. Just nudge it under the sofa where it wouldn't be found. So I nosed it off the table, edged it along the floor and around the back of the television set.

Having made a stand for freedom, it was time to enjoy it with a long snooze. But another smart idea interrupted my good intentions. If they can reprogram me, then I could reprogram them. Not with the same cruelty of course. Just some gentle persuasion to bend them more to my way of thinking.

I scurried back to the television set, nudged the book back out and whipped it off to the kennel. This would require a night of swatting and tactical scheming.

Little Pleasures

These can make a difference to one's day. Along they come, right out of blue sky and bring delight if you let it.

This little pleasure occurred when all untoward activities requiring my professional involvement were temporarily absent. "T" and "L" were safe, the dead letter drop at the front of the house was functioning in the normal deliver and retrieve pattern. Agent E, whose name I now recognize, after that unfortunate incident, as Energex has become 'a known' as we say in the body-guarding industry. There has been no perceived threat to the residence. No excitement at all to send the adrenaline racing. Bodyguard duties must continue as normal even without a spark to liven the day. I know that one should be grateful but having to be grateful for days on end is another matter. One can become slipshod in one's duties, slack on the alert, on guard in the body but absent in the brain.

So what happens? A bundle of feathers arrives to alter this state of affairs. It's black and white, cheeky, sings like an angel, struts around like it owns the place and flies off at a whim. What it also does is trots up to me, bold a you like, darts in and tucks into my morning tea on the verandah. A favourite morsel saved for a mid morning snack. No introduction or civilized request, just a snatch and grab stunt and takes off before I could howl in protest. The audacity of it. After a few moments it returned from its perch on the tree where it had daintily chewed the morsel, *my morsel.* Then it did something unexpected. Took a deep breath, threw back its head and sang a most melodic thank-you. So delightful its misdemeanour was forgotten. Perfectly understood by both parties with nary a word.

Next time, I took a bite of my morning tea and edged it toward my new friend who gobbled it up then gave another thank-you performance for which I replied with a moochy growl—Friend—I think that cosy term is now appropriate.

We meet quite often of late. Share a tidbit because that's all it is now I come to think of it, then together, indulge in a bit of fun. Such a small price to pay to enliven my day.

I have even given my friend a pet name, Maggie. I've heard from "T" and "L", who saw us together one day, that my feathered friend and her sort play more serious games. *Dive bombing*, it's called, when they get into their heads you're a threat. It's not that way between us but I shall take note of that bit of gossip although I'm sure that's all it is, just unkind rumour.

Right now its fly-off time after the present interlude has ended in the usual manner, a farewell thank-you. For me, anchored at ground level, being on the watch all day and half the night will become more enjoyable.

Eavesdropping

I'd been rather restless that morning and was mooching around the house when I heard "L" on the phone. 'Yes, Friday the 12th will be Okay. I'll bring Herbie in. He won't like it but it has to be done.'

Suddenly I felt sick inside. Maybe it was that dead mouse I'd sunk my teeth into. Then something from the back of my mind surfaced and gave me the heebees. That, *'bring Herbie in'* syllable. Did it mean they were mad at me or maybe even tired of me. I flopped on the floor to think it out and eventually came to the conclusion there may have been some questionable behaviour on my part.

It was true I didn't like the neighbour's cat

but that sly tom didn't like me so it was only natural to defend my territory even if it did occasionally spill a drop of blood.

They reckon I smell at times but who doesn't when you roll in the mud. Or was it that I sometimes pinched food off the kitchen bench? Well, you can't leave food on the bench, it's not hygienic so it was only my duty to remove it. Why send me away when the three of us are so happy together?

'What's the big sigh,' "L" said a few hours later. 'Don't look so sad.' I glanced up at her, 'Never mind, Herbie,' she said and patted me on the head. Was that a goodbye gesture? Was it back on the streets again? No, I couldn't bear that. Perhaps I was to be auctioned off like a slave to some cruel master? This has almost spoilt my appetite. I lay on the rug thinking how good life had been since the stardust fell that night. Now it was coming to an end. I sighed, a long, mournful sigh.

Nothing more was said but there was still two days to be endured before Friday. I would be on my best behaviour. At least there would be happy memories. But this did not cheer one little bit.

When Friday morning arrived, "L" backed out the car and clipped me into the back seat. Where we were heading, I didn't care. A few moments later we were at the Vet Clinic, not one of my favourite places—'Euthanasia'—I thought.

They picked me up and placed me on the table. Yes! As I thought, the nurse passed him a hypodermic needle. "L" stood in front of me, probably shielding me from seeing it but I'd kept one eye on him. So this is all the thanks I get for all those hours of faithful guard duty? When I think of all those sleepless nights. At least it will be quick. The Vet felt around my back and neck then stabbed.

I waited to die, at least I'd die with dignity. The seconds ticked by and nothing happened. Where was death? Then I heard an angel's voice and a gentle touch.

'Herbie, the Vet has inserted a microchip so if you get lost, we can easily find you,' "L" said giving me a hug. I sat up. I can hardly believe I'm not going to die. My heart stopped banging. I hopped off the table and headed for the door, "L" right behind me. The world has changed colour. I'm going home because now I've got I.D. for all to see. This little chip could open up new possibilities. Maybe now I could explore a little further afield. Oh, yes! I've been longing to meet that new female, walks past my gate every morning. *A real doll*.

Anyway, point is, I'll sleep real easy tonight, it's all official now, I'm computerised. I can tell the world—Herbie's here to stay. ❧

ATTENTION

Herbie Book 2
will come out in stores in 2012.

Register if you would like to be
informed as soon as it becomes available.
It's simple—Just send a blank email to:

herbiebook2@bigpond.com

and in the subject line write:

**"Please inform me of
Herbie Book 2 availability."**
